TABLE OF CONTENTS

© 2013 Hobart Institute of Welding Technology

ISBN 978-1-936058-20-4

D1211071

GLOSSARY OF WELDING TERMS

Acceptable Weld – A weld meeting the applicable requirements.

Arc Voltage (arc welding) – The electrical potential between the electrode and workpiece.

As-Welded, adj. – Pertaining to the condition of weldments prior to subsequent thermal, mechanical, or chemical treatments

Automatic Welding (W-AU) – See automatic process.

Automatic Process (XXXX-AU) – An operation performed with equipment requiring occasional or no observation and no manual adjustment during its operation. Variations of this term are automatic brazing, automatic soldering, automatic thermal cutting, automatic thermal spraying, and automatic welding.

Backgouging – The removal of weld metal and base metal from the weld root side of a welded joint to facilitate complete fusion and complete joint penetration upon subsequent welding from that side.

Backing – A material or device placed against the back side of the joint adjacent to the joint root, or at both sides of a joint in electroslag and electrogas welding, to support and shield molten weld metal. The material may be partially fused or remain unfused during welding and may be either metal or nonmetal.

Backing Weld – Backing in the form of a weld.

Base Metal Zone (BMZ) – The portion of base metal adjacent to a weld, braze or solder joint or thermal cut and unaffected by welding, brazing, soldering, or thermal cutting.

Bevel Angle – The angle between the bevel of a joint member and a plane perpendicular to the surface of the member.

Bevel Face – The prepared surface of a bevel edge shape.

Brazing Procedure Qualification Record (BPQR) – A record of brazing variables used to produce an acceptable test brazement and the results of tests conducted on the brazement to qualify a brazing procedure specification.

Defect – A discontinuity or discontinuities that by nature or accumulated effect render a part or product unable to meet minimum applicable acceptance standards or specifications. The term designates rejectability.

Direct Current Electrode Negative (DCEN) – The arrangement of direct current arc welding leads in which the electrode is the negative pole and workpiece is the positive pole of the welding arc.

Direct Current Electrode Positive (DCEP) – The arrangement of direct current arc welding leads in which the electrode is the positive pole and the workpiece is the negative pole of the welding arc.

Discontinuity – An interruption of the typical structure of a material, such as a lack of homogeneity in its mechanical, metallurgical, or physical characteristics. A discontinuity is not necessarily a defect.

Edge Preparation – The preparation of the edges of the joint members, by cutting, cleaning, plating, or other means.

Face Reinforcement – Weld reinforcement on the side of the joint from which welding was done.

Flaw – An undesirable discontinuity.

Flux – A material applied to the workpiece(s) before or during joining or surfacing to cause interactions that remove oxides and other contaminants, improve wetting, and affect the final surface profile. Welding flux may also affect the weld metal chemical composition.

Globular Transfer (gas metal arc welding) – The transfer of molten metal in large drops from a consumable electrode across the arc.

Groove Angle – The included angle between the groove faces of a weld groove.

Groove Face – Any surface in a weld groove prior to welding.

Groove Radius – A nonstandard term when used for bevel radius.

Heat-Affected Zone (HAZ) – The portion of base metal whose mechanical properties or microstructure have been altered by the heat of welding, brazing, soldering, or thermal cutting.

Interpass Temperature (welding) – In a multipass weld, the temperature of the weld area between weld passes.

Joint Design – The shape, dimensions, and configuration of the joint.

Layer – A stratum of weld metal consisting of one or more weld beads.

Machine Welding – A nonstandard term when used for mechanized welding.

Manual Welding (W-MA) – See manual process.

Manual Process (XXXX-MA) – An operation with the torch, gun, or electrode holder held and manipulated by hand. Accessory equipment, such as part motion devices and handheld filler material feeders may be used. Variations of this term are manual brazing, manual soldering, manual thermal cutting, manual thermal spraying, and manual welding.

Mechanized Process (XXXX-ME) – An operation with equipment requiring manual adjustment by an operator in response to visual observation, with the torch, gun, wire guide assembly, or electrode holder held by a mechanical device.

Peening – The mechanical working of metals using impact blows.

Postheating – The application of heat to an assembly after brazing, soldering, thermal spraying, thermal cutting, or welding.

Preheat, n. – The heat applied to the workpiece(s) to attain and maintain the preheat temperature prior to joining, thermal cutting, or thermal spraying.

Prequalified Welding Procedure Specification (PWPS) – A welding procedure specification in compliance with the stipulated conditions of a particular welding code or specification and therefore acceptable for use under that code or specification without a requirement for qualification testing.

Procedure Qualification – The demonstration that the use of prescribed joining processes, materials, and techniques will result in a joint exhibiting specified soundness and mechanical properties.

Procedure Qualification Record (PQR) – See brazing procedure qualification record and welding procedure qualification record.

Residual Stress – Stress present in a joint member or material that is free of external forces or thermal gradients.

Root Face – The portion of the groove face within the joint root.

Root Opening – A separation at the joint root between the workpieces.

Root Reinforcement – Weld reinforcement opposite the side from which welding was done.

Semiautomatic Process (XXXX-SA) – An operation performed manually with equipment controlling one or more of the process conditions.

Shielding Gas – A gas used to produce a protective atmosphere.

Short Circuiting Transfer (gas metal arc welding) – Metal transfer in which molten metal from a consumable electrode is deposited during repeated short circuits. See also globular transfer and spray transfer.

Spray Transfer (gas metal arc welding) – Metal transfer in which molten metal from a consumable electrode is propelled axially across the arc in small droplets.

Standard Welding Procedure Specification (SWPS) – A welding procedure specification qualified according to the requirements of AWS B2.1, approved by AWS, and made available for production welding by companies or individuals other than those performing the qualification test.

Stress-Relief Heat Treatment – Uniform heating of a structure or a portion thereof to a sufficient temperature to relieve the major portion of the residual stresses, followed by uniform cooling.

Tack Weld – A weld made to hold the parts of a weldment in proper alignment until the final welds are made.

Test Coupon – A weldment, brazement, or solderment used for procedure or performance qualification testing.

Weld, n. – A localized coalescence of metals or nonmetals produced either by heating the materials to the welding temperature, with or without the application of pressure, or by the application of pressure alone and with or without the use of filler material.

Weldability – The capacity of material to be welded under the imposed fabrication conditions into a specific, suitably designed structure performing satisfactorily in the intended service.

Welding Procedure – The detailed methods and practices involved in the production of a weldment.

Welding Procedure Qualification Record (WPQR) – A record of welding variables used to produce an acceptable test weldment and the results of tests conducted on the weldment to qualify a welding procedure specification.

Welding Procedure Specification (WPS) – A document providing the required welding variables fur a specific application to assure repeatability by properly trained welders and welding operators.

Welding Sequence – The order of making welds in a weldment.

Welding Technique – Details of the welding operation controlled by the welder or welding operator.

Welding Test Position – The orientation of a weld joint for welding procedure or welder qualification testing.

Weldment – An assembly joined by welding.

Weld Metal Zone (WMZ) – The portion of the weld area consisting of weld metal.

Weld Pass – A single progression of welding along a joint. The result of a weld pass is a weld bead or layer.

Welder – One who performs manual or semiautomatic welding.

Welder Certification – Written verification that a welder has produced welds meeting a prescribed standard of welder performance.

Welder Performance Qualification – The demonstration of a welder's or welding operator's ability to produce welds meeting prescribed standards.

Welding Procedure Qualification Record (WPQR) – A record of welding variables used to produce an acceptable test weldment and the results of tests conducted on the weldment to qualify a welding procedure specification.

Welder Registration – The act of registering a welder certification or a photostatic copy of the welder certification.

Welding Operator – One who operates adaptive control, automatic, mechanized, or robotic welding equipment.

WELD TEST POSITIONS

Fillet Welds

FLAT POSITION 1F	HORIZONTAL POSITION 2F	VERTICAL POSITION 3F	OVERHEAD POSITION 4F
Axis of Weld Horizontal	Axis of Weld Horizontal	Axis of Weld Vertical	Axis of Weld Horizontal

Groove Welds

FLAT POSITION 1G	HORIZONTAL POSITION 2G	VERTICAL POSITION 3G	OVERHEAD POSITION 4G
Plates, Axis of Weld Horizontal	Plates vertical, Axis of Weld Horizontal	Plates vertical, Axis of Weld Vertical	Plates Overhead, Axis of Weld Horizontal

FLAT 1G	HORIZONTAL 2G	HORIZONTAL FIXED 5G	45° FIXED 6G
		"Bell Hole"	"Arkansas Bell Hole"
			45° ±5°
Pipe *shall be turned or rolled* while welding axis of pipe horizontal	Axis of Pipe Vertical	Pipe *shall not be turned or rolled* while welding axis of pipe horizontal	Pipe stationary with axis approximately 45°

THE PURPOSE OF WELDING PROCEDURES AND QUALIFICATION

Objective: To identity the various types of welding qualifications and the development steps in performing qualification work.

A Welding Procedure provides detailed information about the methods and practices involved in the production of a weldment, including step-by-step directions on how to assemble the components of a weldment.

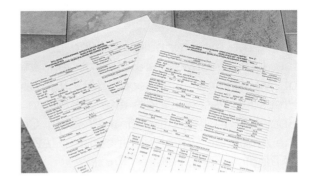

A Welding Procedure ensures quality, increases productivity, reduces weld cost, provides for repeatability and uniformity in production, and details proper mechanical properties of a weldment.

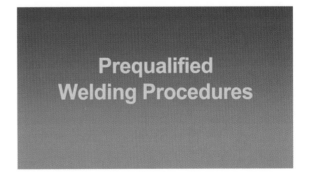

Welding Procedure
• Ensures quality
• Increases productivity
• Reduces weld cost
• Provides for repeatability and uniformity
• Details proper mechanical properties

Many welding codes require that procedures be written and qualified before welding can begin.

Some codes, however, do not require qualification tests. These are commonly called Prequalified Welding Procedures.

Prequalified Welding Procedures

For example, the American Welding Society Structural Welding Code allows the use of prequalified procedures – usually based on the use of specific processes.

A building constructed to AWS D-1.1 code requirements, is one such example.

The three most popular welding codes used in the United States are: the American Society of Mechanical Engineers' (ASME) Boiler and Pressure Vessel Code, the American Welding Society's (AWS) Structural Welding Code, and the American Petroleum Institute's (API) Welding of Pipelines and Related Facilities.

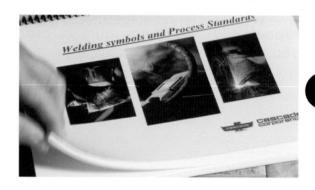

Welding Codes

- ASME Boiler & Pressure Vessel Code
- AWS Structural Welding Code
- API Standard for Welding Pipelines and Related Facilities

Many companies prepare a quality assurance manual, which determines the code or quality standard to be used for qualification. It assigns responsibility for procedure and welder qualification preparation, review and approval, and also provides a system for revision and continuing communication.

Even when codes do not apply, Welding Procedures improve the efficiency of welding fabrication. The American Welding Society has developed a specification called Welding Procedure and Performance Qualification, identified as AWS B-2.1, to assist with the development of procedures in non-code areas.

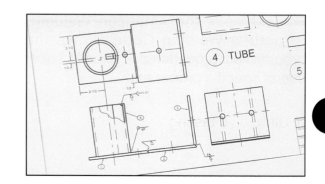

The development of a Welding Procedure begins with the analysis of the weldment design; which establishes the type, size, and location of the welds.

Once the particular weld joints are selected and described, a Welding Procedure Specification, commonly abbreviated WPS, is written.

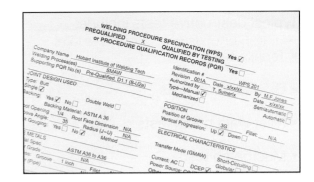

There are several software packages available for this process. Procedures are often created on a computer and then printed for end use.

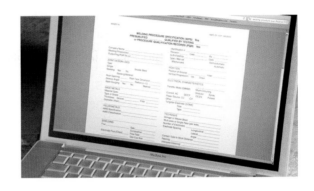

The WPS lists all variables affecting mechanical, chemical, and metallurgical properties of the welded joint. These variables include materials, welding process, machine setting, joint design, and welding technique – and are sometimes referred to as essential or nonessential, and supplementary variables, although the actual names for these elements vary from code to code.

To qualify the Welding Procedure, a highly skilled welder prepares and welds one or more test specimens following the requirements outlined in the written procedure. The actual requirements are based on the applicable code, or in the case of a non-code application, the companies' quality requirements. The welded specimen could require nondestructive or destructive testing.

Typical code qualifying nondestructive testing may include:

• Visual inspection

• Radiographic testing

• Ultrasonic testing

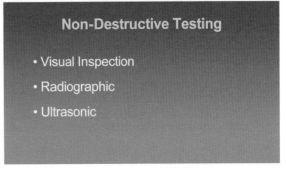

Typical destructive tests include:

• Tensile tests

• Guided bend tests

• Fillet weld break tests

• Macroetch tests

The skill of a welder is evaluated through various testing procedures called a Performance Qualification. Performance Qualification is the demonstration of a welder's ability to produce welds that meet specific standards.

Weld specifications vary from code to code, consequently, the qualification of a welder under one code, will not necessarily qualify the welder under another code – even though the testing may be similar. A universal welding qualification does not exist.

To qualify a welder's skills, the welder is required to produce test coupons that meet the requirements detailed in a specific welding procedure. The test coupons must first pass visual inspection, followed by destructive and/or other nondestructive testing methods based on specific code requirements.

Welders cannot be qualified on their own. A company appointed representative must witness the performance qualification in accordance with the WPS, and then record the test results.

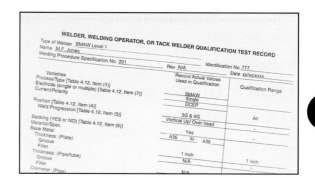

TOPIC 1 REVIEW QUESTIONS

1. **Arrange the following items in the order in which they occur:**

   Certify Welder   1. _____

   Qualify Procedure   2. _____

   Analyze Design   3. _____

   Write Welding Procedure Specification   4. _____

   Qualify Welder   5. _____

2. **Describe the difference between welder qualification and welder certification:**

   _____

   _____

   _____

   _____

   _____

3. **Who is responsible for procedure and welder qualification?**

   _____

4. **Describe the difference between procedure qualification and welder qualification:**

   _____

   _____

   _____

   _____

   _____

5. **What two important elements are controlled through development of welding procedures?**

   1. _____ 2. _____

WELDING PROCEDURE SPECIFICATIONS

Objective: To identify the elements which are included in a welding procedure specification to control weld quality.

A Welding Procedure Specification is a step-by-step description of how to produce a weld.

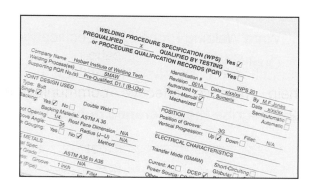

A typical Welding Procedure includes detailed information about:

- Process and method of application

- Material specifications and thickness

- Filler metal type

- Flux (if applicable)

- Shielding gas

- Welding position

- Weld size and pass sequence

- Weld current and polarity

- Voltage and travel speed

- Travel direction

- Preheating and interpass temperature

- Postheating

- Joint preparation and cleaning

- Peening

- Inspection and repair

Welding Procedure
- Process and method of application
- Material specifications and thickness
- Filler metal type
- Flux
- Shielding gas
- Welding position
- Weld size and pass sequence

Welding Procedure
- Weld current and polarity
- Voltage and travel speed
- Travel direction
- Preheating and interpass temperature control
- Postheating

Welding Procedure
- Joint preparation and cleaning
- Peening
- Inspection and repair

At the top of most Welding Procedure Specification forms, you will find the name of the company and company representative preparing the procedure specification. If a code is used, the title of the code is shown.

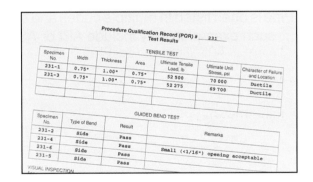

Each Procedure Specification must have an Identification Number. Identification Numbers help maintain effective communication and accurate record keeping.

Revision numbers assure that the most current copy of a procedure is in use.

Some Specification forms include Procedure Qualification Records, which show the results of qualification tests.

Of course, if the procedure is prequalified, this does not apply.

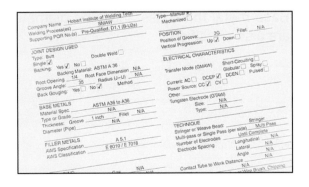

A WPS also lists and describes welding variables. These variables will change from code to code, for example, some codes refer to items as essential or nonessential.

One of the most important variables described in a Welding Procedure, is the welding process. Shielded metal, gas tungsten, or gas metal arc welding are just some of the many process options.

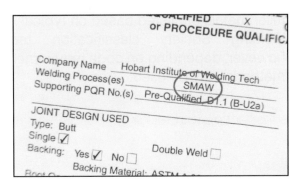

The method of application is also important. Will the process be applied manually, semi-automatically, mechanized, or automatically?

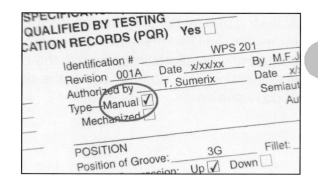

Base metals are often listed using ASTM standards – such as A36 or A53.

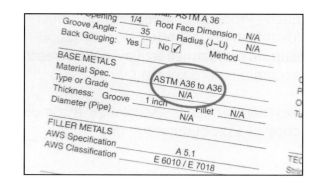

Pipe is often listed in multiple codes and standards … such examples may include API or ASME.

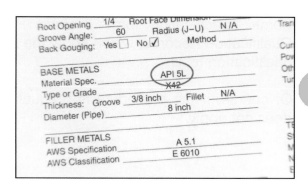

Base metal thickness and pipe diameter ranges are also specified.

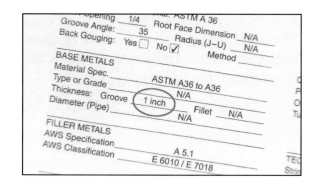

Filler metals are listed based on typical American Welding Society classification techniques, however, depending on code requirements, other methods may be used.

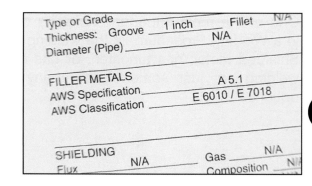

Shielding gas is listed by type and grade. For example, welding grade carbon dioxide may be shown for use with the gas metal arc welding process.

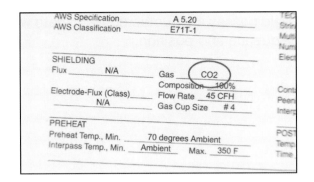

Flux is a material used by some processes to shield the weld pool. It is specified using an AWS classification number in combination with an electrode wire classification number.

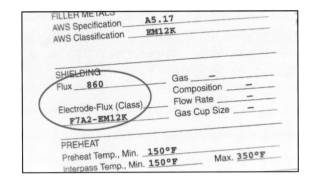

Welding position is listed and, depending on the code being used, will sometimes give information for several weld beads.

The welding procedure also indicates whether vertical position welding will use downhill or uphill travel. This is commonly called welding progression.

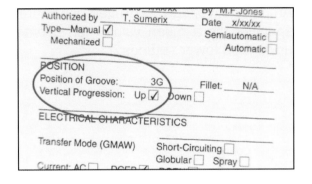

Joint design is shown with an attached sketch that details groove angles, root faces, root openings and other dimensions.

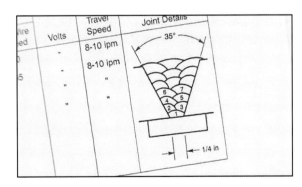

For groove welds, the joint design may indicate that a backing strip is required. In most instances, the omission of backing material requires the development and qualification of a new procedure.

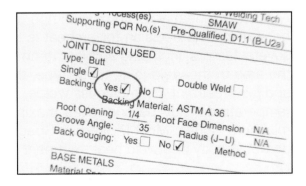

EW512-3

Weld passes are numbered to indicate weld bead sequence and position.

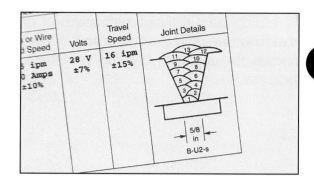

The numbered passes are then normally referenced to a table that lists the technique, electrode size, amperage, voltage, and travel speed for each pass.

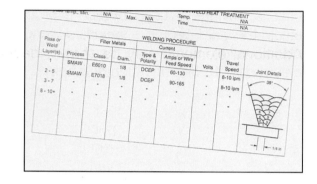

Amperage, voltage and travel speeds are normally specified as a mean value – an average of the upper and lower settings.

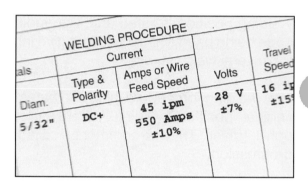

The type of electrical current – DCEP, DCEN, or alternating current – may be included on the WPS.

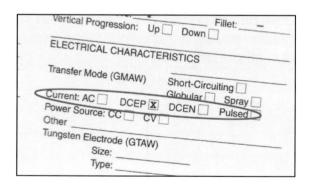

At times, preheat and interpass temperatures will be shown. The decision for preheat is based on several factors, including ambient temperature in the area of the weld joint, metal type, thickness, and joint restraint. On multipass welds, interpass temperatures may be shown as maximum and minimum values. Most Procedure Specifications do not specify postweld heat treatment.

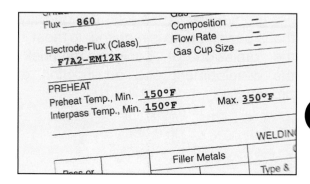

A WPS includes information on joint preparation, cleaning between multipass welds, and cleaning prep tools - such as chipping hammers, grinders, air chisels, and wire brushes.

Electrode Spacing			
	Longitudinal		N/A
	Lateral		N/A
	Angle		N/A
Contact Tube to Work Distance			N/A
Peening	N/A		
Interpass Cleaning:	Power Wire Brush, Chipping		

POSTWELD HEAT TREATMENT
Temp. _____ N/A
Time _____ N/A

PROCEDURE

These are just some of the elements that could be included in a Welding Procedure Specification. Additional elements may be shown, depending on the complexity of the work to be performed.

You should also realize that the development of a Welding Procedure Specification is greatly affected by the code that is required for a product or weldment, although the variables or elements of the procedure are always similar.

WELDING PROCEDURE SPECIFICATION

Company Name: _____ Prepared By: _____

Welding Code: _____ Date_____

WPS No: _____ Revision No: _____ Date of Revision: _____

Supporting Procedure Qualification Record: _____

Welding Process: _____

Method of Application: _____

Base Metal Specification: _____

Base Metal Thickness Range: _____

Filler Metal Specification: _____

Filler Metal Classification: _____

Single or Multiple Arc: _____

Shielding Gas: _____ Flux Type: _____

Welding Position: _____

Progression of Welding: _____

Preheat and Interpass Temperature Control: _____

_____

Post Weld Heat Treatment: _____

_____

Joint Preparation: _____

_____

Cleaning:_____

_____

Root Treatment: _____

Peening:_____

Appearance of Weld Layers: _____

_____

Repair: _____

_____

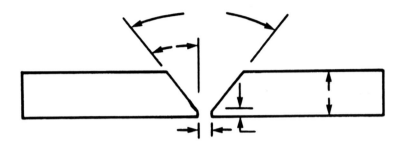

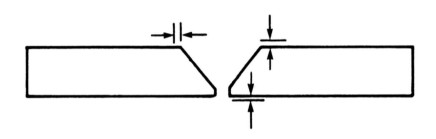

Bead No.	Electrode or Wire Type	Electrode or Wire Size	Current Polarity	Amps	Volts	Travel Speed In/Min	Technique	Welding Direction	Gas Flow Rate CFH

TOPIC 2 REVIEW QUESTIONS

1. List ten elements which are normally listed on the welding procedure specification:

1. _____

2. _____

3. _____

4. _____

5. _____

6. _____

7. _____

8. _____

9. _____

10. _____

2. What type of procedure does not require testing?

_____

_____

_____

3. Why are reference numbers assigned to welding procedure specification?

_____

_____

_____

PROCEDURE QUALIFICATION RECORDS

Objective: To know the methods of qualifying a welding procedure specification to verify that welding materials and methods are used to produce weld quality.

Procedure Qualification Records are used to demonstrate that a welding procedure can meet the prescribed quality standards established by a welding code, or company quality standard.

Generally, welding procedures can be either qualified or prequalified.

Prequalified procedures do not require destructive or nondestructive tests. Instead, the reliability of these procedures is based on proven past experiences using code-specified variables.

Prequalified procedures are recognized only by a few codes, one of which is the AWS D1.1 Strutural Welding Code.

Qualified procedures utilize tests to prove the quality of a weld.

When a procedure is required to be qualified, a Procedures Qualification Record, or "PQR", is used to document the method of welding and the test results.

PQR forms are often contained within a WPS.

Procedure Qualifications specify weld pass number, amperage, voltage, travel speed and other pertinent information.

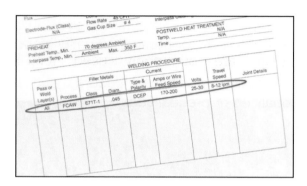

Some variables such as welding process and welding position are commonly designated as essential, meaning that the revision of these variables would require requalification of the procedure.

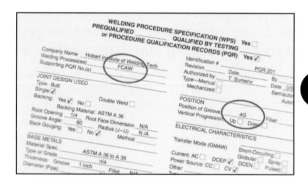

To qualify the welding procedure, a skilled welder must first produce a sample weld following the WPS variables. Note that the samples may not resemble the actual weld. For example, a corner joint may be used in construction, but due to the difficulties of testing, may be replaced by a butt or T-joint during qualification. The number, size and thickness of test samples will vary depending on the type of weld and the code requirements.

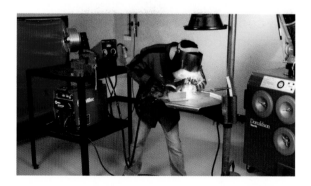

Test samples are first visually inspected for porosity, undercut, cracks, overlap, and other discontinuities.

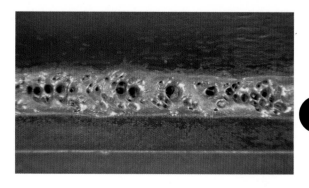

The inspection will determine if the discontinuities are defects, and if they should be rejected per specified code requirements.

Following visual inspection, other nondestructive tests may be utilized. Radiography and ultrasonic tests are commonly used for Procedure Qualifications.

Most codes require some form of destructive testing, such as a bend test or tensile test, to ensure joint and weld soundness.

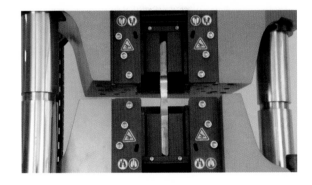

The code or company standard will specify the number of tests, the test coupon sizes, location of the samples on the coupon, and the testing method.

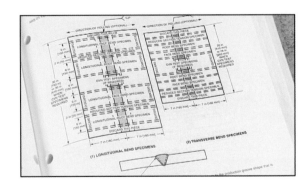

Each tested specimen is then evaluated in accordance with code requirements to determine quality and acceptability standards.

Once the test coupons have been evaluated, important data such as type, size, and number of discontinuities are recorded on the PQR.

If the weld passes all the required tests, the procedure is qualified.

A company appointed representative then signs the Procedure Qualification Record indicating the test welds were prepared, welded and tested according to the applicable code requirements.

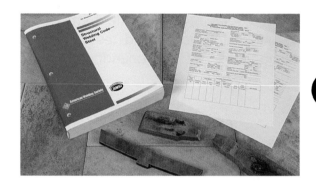

The qualification of the welding procedure proves the materials and methods used to produce a particular weld will provide the required quality based on the governing specification or code.

PROCEDURE QUALIFICATION RECORD (PQR)

Company Name: _____

Procedure Qualification Record No: _____ Date_____

Material specification _____   Shielding gas _____ Flow rate _____

Welding process _____   Single or multiple pass _____

Method of application _____   Single or multiple arc _____

Position of welding _____   Welding current _____

Filler Metal specification _____   Welding progression _____

Filler Metal classification _____   Preheat temperature _____

                                                    Postheat treatment _____

Pass No.	Electrode Size	Welding Current		Speed of Travel	Joint Detail
		Amps	Volts		

TEST RESULTS

Visual Test

Appearance:	Undercut:	Porosity:

Radiographic or Ultrasonic Examination

RT Report No:	UT Report No:

Tensile Test

Specimen No.	Width	Thickness	Area	Ultimate Total Load (lb)	Ultimate Unit Stress (psi)	Character of Failure & Location

Guided Bend Tests

Type and Figure No.	Result

Other Tests

Type of Test	
Deposit Analysis	
Other	

Welder's Name _____

Welder I.D. No. _____

Laboratory Test No. _____

Test Date _____

Witnessed by _____

Manufacturer or Contractor _____

Authorized by _____

Date _____

TOPIC 3 REVIEW QUESTIONS

1. What written report is used to indicate the quality of a weld produced by a welding procedure specification?

   _____

   _____

2. Name at least three nondestructive testing processes which could be used to qualify a procedure:

   1. _____

   2. _____

   3. _____

3. Name two common tests used to qualify fillet weld procedures.

   1. _____

   2. _____

4. What two destructive tests are used to evaluate groove weld procedure?

   1. _____

   2. _____

5. What document acts as a guideline to determine the type of test, the number of tests, the method of test and standards of quality to qualify procedure?

   _____

   _____

   _____

PERFORMANCE QUALIFICATION

Objective: To identify the variables which are described on welder, welding operator and tack welder qualification reports, and describe the process of performance qualification.

The primary purpose of Performance Qualification is to measure the skill and ability of a welder.

Like Procedure Qualifications, Welder Qualifications are performed prior to the start of production.

Welders are required to demonstrate their skills by using prequalified or qualified procedures to prepare sample welds.

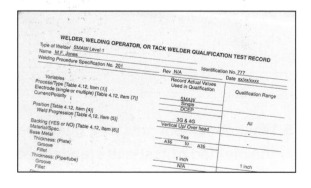

The sample welds are tested and evaluated according to the specified quality and guidelines for the job. The guidelines could be a published code or company standard.

Let's examine a sample welder qualification record.

At the top of most welder qualification records are spaces for the welder's name and identification number.

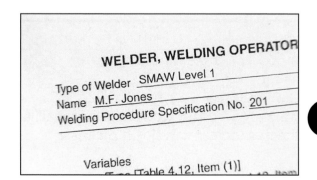

Next, the base metal type is shown using an ASTM or ASME number designation.

Base metal thickness is also important, since multipass welds on thicker metals require greater skill than single pass welds on thinner metals.

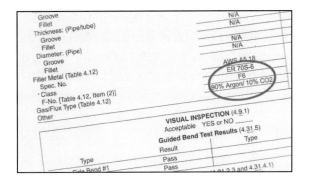

Filler metal classification, size, type of shielding (whether flux or gas), are also specified.

Shielded metal arc welding electrodes are grouped using a series of "F" numbers. The F1 group consists of iron powder electrodes, F2's are rutile-sodium electrodes, F3's are cellulosic electrodes and F4's are low hydrogen. The higher the F number, the greater the difficulty and required skill. Generally, welders are qualified to weld with electrodes equal to, or lower than, the F number shown in the Welder Qualification Record.

SMAW Electrodes
Grouped using "F" numbers
- F1: Iron Powder
- F2: Rutile-Sodium
- F3: Cellulosic
- F4: Low Hydrogen

(welders are qualified to weld with electrodes equal to, or lower than, the number shown in the Welder Qualification Record)

Shielding gases and electrode types, are essential variables in gas shielded processes. Normally welders must be qualified for each electrode and shielding gas combination.

Welding processes and methods of application are also essential variables in the qualifications of a welder. Welders are required to qualify for each welding process and method. For example a welder who is qualified using the flux cored arc welding process, would not be qualified to use the gas metal arc welding process.

Welding Processes and Methods of Application
- A welder who is qualified using FCAW would not be qualified to use GMAW
- A welder using a SMAW manual process would not be qualified to use a semi-automatic GMAW process

Welding position is shown on the welder qualification record because it also determines skill level. Welders are often qualified in the more difficult positions, such as vertical and overhead, and as a result, are automatically qualified in the easier flat and horizontal positions. Qualification of more than one position with one test, however, depends on the applicable code.

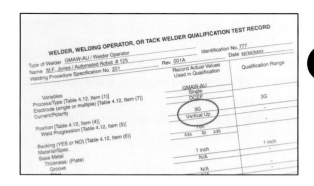

Along with position, the type of weld must be analyzed. Fillet welds are considered to be less difficult than groove welds. Consequently, welders qualified to produce groove welds, are often also qualified to produce fillet welds.

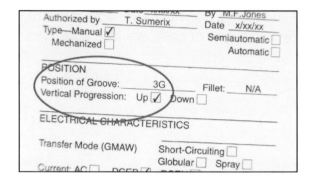

A series of numbers and digits are used to indicate position and weld type. For example; 1G indicates a flat position groove weld, 2G indicates horizontal position groove weld and so on. "G" stands for groove, while "F" would indicate a fillet weld.

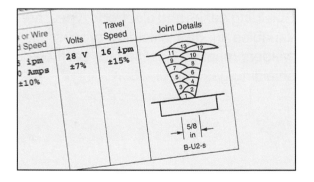

Position and Weld Type

- 1G: Flat Position Groove Weld
- 2G: Horizontal Position Groove Weld

- G: Groove Weld
- F: Fillet Weld

When welding is to be done in the vertical position, a direction of travel is usually specified, since the skills required to weld vertical up are different from those required to weld vertical down.

Backing strips are sometimes used to support molten metal, and help with making full penetration welds on groove or butt joints.

Welders qualified to produce open root groove welds are also qualified to deposit welds on joints fitted with backing strips. However, welders qualified for backing strips are usually not qualified to weld open-root grooves.

Electrical current is also specified on Welder Qualifications. Changes in type of electrical current may require requalification due to changes in arc characteristics that affect the welder's skill.

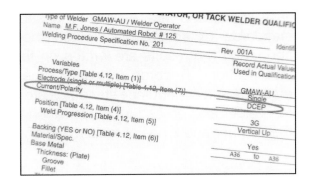

Once the variables are known, the welder prepares a sample weld according to the procedure.

The specimen may be visually inspected for undercut, lack of penetration, porosity, cracks, and other defects.

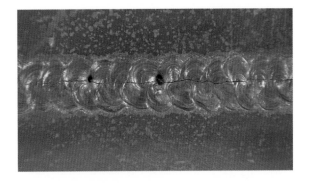

It may also undergo nondestructive tests including radiographic evaluation.

Destructive testing, however, is the most common method used to evaluate a welder's skill.

Test specimens are evaluated based on the standards of acceptability established in the code, and the results are written on the Welder Qualification Records. Usually the testing methods and acceptance standards are the same for welder and procedure qualification, although the number and types of tests may vary.

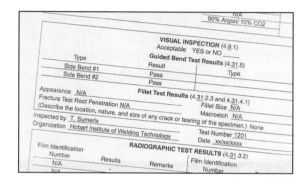

Once the record is complete, a company representative signs the record verifying that preparation, welding and testing were completed and met the code requirements.

Welding operators who perform automated welding activities must also pass qualification tests. However, since many automated operations require only basic welding skills, fewer variables are included in the welding operator qualification record.

Typical essential variables include identification of base metal type, welding process, type of electrode, type of shielding, and welding position.

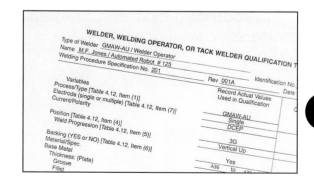

Testing and evaluation are similar to other welder qualification records, and ultimately indicate conformance or nonconformance.

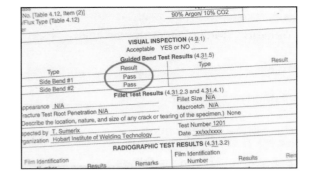

In some situations, welders may need to be retested and requalified.

For instance, if a Welding Procedure is significantly modified – the welder may require a new qualification.

Additionally, some codes specify that the welder must use a welding process within a set period of time to maintain qualification status. Welders may also have to requalify if their quality has been questioned.

Finally, it is important to mention that companies often require periodic requalification testing to assure their own quality standards.

WELDER AND WELDING OPERATOR QUALIFICATION TEST RECORD

Welder or Welding Operator's Name: _____ **Identification No:** _____

Welding Process: _____

Method of Application: _____

Base Metal Specification: _____

Base Metal Thickness Range: _____ **Diameter (if pipe)** _____

Filler Metal Specification: _____

Filler Metal Classification: _____ **Diameter:** _____ **F No:** _____

Flux Type: _____ **Shielding Gas Type:** _____

Welding Position: _____ **Welding Progression:** _____ **Backing Strip:** _____

In Accordance with Welding Procedure Specification No: _____

Visual Inspection		
Appearance:	Undercut:	Piping Porosity:

Guided Bend Test Results			
Type	Result	Type	Result

Fillet Test Results	
Appearance	Fillet Size
Fracture Test Root Penetration	Macroetch

Radiographic Test Results					
Film Identification	Results	Remarks	Film Identification	Results	Remarks

Test Conducted by: _____ **Per:** _____ **Test No:** _____

In Accordance with: _____

Manufacturer or Contractor _____ **Authorized by:** _____ **Date:** _____

TOPIC 4 REVIEW QUESTIONS

1. What type of qualification is used to measure the skills of persons producing small welds to hold parts of a weldment in the proper location prior to final weld deposits?

   _____

   _____

2. Which type of qualification is used to measure the skill of people performing manual and semiautomatic welding?

   _____

   _____

3. Name five welding variables which are included on the welder qualification record.

   1. _____

   2. _____

   3. _____

   4. _____

   5. _____

4. People who perform mechanized or automatic welding methods are normally called:

   _____

   _____

5. Describe three situations which may require the welder to requalify:

   1. _____

   2. _____

   3. _____

MAINTAINING QUALIFICATION RECORDS

Objective: To know the importance of accurate, effective recording of procedures and qualification records and the method used to provide for record maintenance.

Weldments can be simple or complex. Obviously, complex weldments require more procedures and the task of accurate record keeping can become difficult.

Manufacturing companies will typically create production manuals to detail the procedures used during product fabrication.

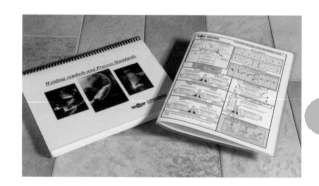

The procedures are numbered and cross-referenced in a table of contents to promote quick retrieval of information.

WPS Number	Product Name	Part Number
		45373
WPS 1-201	Widget	49442
WPS 1-202	CFM	49441
WPS 1-203	LPT	54956
WPS 1-204	Wing nut assembly	49443
WPS 1-205	Clutch assembly	49457
	Pressure plate	

For instance, a welding procedure number found in a table of contents, is often placed in the tail bracket of welding symbol.

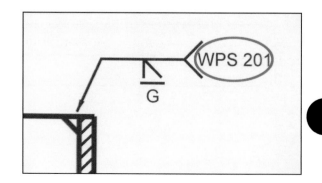

When a company is about to manufacture a new product, several questions must be answered to accurately establish production processes and costs.

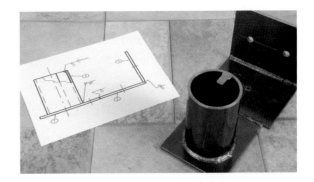

First, the company must determine if they have previously worked to the product's quality specifications or welding code. If not, new procedures will be required.

Establishing Production Processes & Costs
- Company must determine if they've previously worked to the product's specifications or welding code
- If not, new procedures will be required

If the company has previously worked with the applicable code, they must then examine the current product design; including base metal, weld type, weld position, and welding processes. If the essential variables are different from the WPS, the new product must be analyzed to determine whether the procedure requires a new qualification.

Next, Welder Qualifications need to be reviewed. If the existing procedures are acceptable, then no further qualifications are required. However, if significant changes have been made to the welding variables, and new procedures have been established, a new qualification will be required. These are just some of the factors that must be examined before production can begin.

Establishing Production Processes & Costs
- Welder Qualifications need to be reviewed
- If existing procedures are acceptable; no further qualifications are required
- If changes have been made and new procedures have been established; qualifications will be required

Reporting and recording the results of qualification tests are also important responsibilities of a manufacturing company.

Qualification forms must be accurate and signed in ink or inspector-stamped by the appropriate company representative. Any revised procedures must be approved.

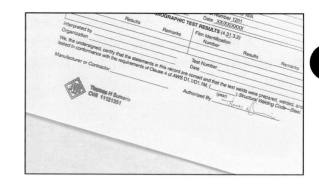

If the variable being changed is not outside the existing limit, the change is made on the Welding Procedure Specification, a revision number is added, and no requalification is needed.

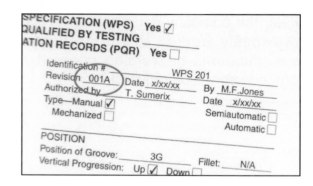

Welding Procedures are prepared and qualified during the design of the product or weldment. The engineering department should be aware of the procedures to assure production is accurate and efficient.

Manufacturing personnel also require copies of the procedures to make sure work is performed using the proper methods, materials and techniques.

Quality Control uses codes to measure the results of a welding operation.

For optimum product quality and efficient manufacturing, Welder Qualification Reports should also be shared between departments.

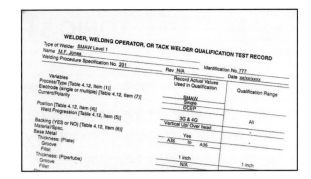

In some cases, the personnel department may require Qualification Reports to evaluate the performance of an individual.

In contract work, the owner or customer may require Welder Qualification Records to insure quality workmanship.

The development of welding procedures and qualifications is extremely important to the success of a company. Equally important, however, is the process of record keeping to prevent duplication of work, and to improve efficiency and organization.

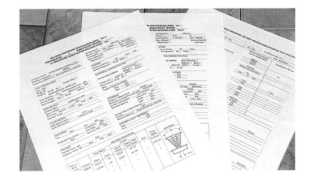

TOPIC 5 REVIEW QUESTIONS

Circle the correct answer.

1. **Why do manufacturing or construction personnel require copies of the procedures and welder qualification reports?**

   A. To maintain accurate files.

   B. To better understand company policy.

   C. To insure welding is performed using approved methods and techniques.

   D. To satisfy legal requirements.

2. **Why does quality control require copies of procedures and welder qualification reports?**

   A. To measure the results of welding operations.

   B. To produce product quality.

   C. To improve field and production inspection techniques.

   D. To avoid field and production inspection.

3. **Revised welding procedure specifications which require requalification:**

   A. Must be requalified prior to use.

   B. Must have a revision number assigned.

   C. Must be completely communicated.

   D. All of the above.

4. **Qualification reports and forms must be:**

   A. Signed in ink by an authorized company representative.

   B. Signed by the president.

   C. Copyrighted.

   D. Notarized.

5. **Arrange the following questions in the proper sequence of consideration by placing numbers beside the question.**

   __ Are welders qualified?

   __ Have we used the code before?

   __ Do qualified procedures exist?